COCK ROBIN

D0511530

A Nature Story by David Stephen
Illustrated by Marjorie Blamey

CUBS

COLLINS COLOUR CUBS

C ock Robin's garden was in
the country and many birds
lived in it. Woodmouse Lane began at
the bottom and led past Squirrel Wood
to Frog's Pond at the other end.

Of course, it wasn't really Cock Robin's garden but that was the way he looked upon it, and during the winter he wouldn't allow another robin into it. If another robin did come along Cock Robin puffed out his red breast at it in warning and drove it away. The garden was his *Territory*, at least as far as the other robins were concerned.

But he was friendly with all the other birds, which means he hardly noticed them and didn't try to drive them out. He had a lot of neighbours—tits, dunnocks, sparrows, starlings, black-birds and chaf-finches. Even woodpigeons. Every day a wood-pecker came to feed on a marrow bone tied to the leg of the bird table.

The owner of the garden had put up the bird table for the winter, and most of the birds visited it many times each day, even when there was no frost or snow. The tits seemed to spend most of their time there, from daylight until dusk. Cock Robin was a regular visitor to the table, where the owner of the garden put out mealworms for him every day. Of course he ate other food as well. But all robins are specially fond of mealworms, so if you have a robin in your garden and want to make friends with it, give it mealworms and you will be sure to win it over.

The birds in the garden
hardly ever quarrelled
with each other,
although the starlings
would sometimes come
along in a body, jostling
the smaller ones off the
table and stirring them
all up. There was enough
food for all—peanuts for
the tits, mealworms for
Cock Robin, a bone for
the woodpecker, raisins
for the blackbirds, and
grain for the pheasants
and woodpigeons. The
owner always laid out
poultry food for the
waterhens that came
from Frog's Pond.

A mole came into the garden, and within a few days moleheaps began to appear along the front of the house. Cock Robin could see the crumbly soil trickling from the top of the newest moleheap when the mole was heaving underneath. One day he watched a blackbird pulling a fat earthworm out of one of the moleheaps. The worm had been thrown up by the burrowing mole, who would surely have poked his face out to get it back again, but the blackbird was there first and pulled it out before the mole could reach it.

Now—Cock Robin was a bright little
bird, and as good a copy-cat as any-
body. So, if the blackbird could find
a worm in the moleheap, there was no
reason why he shouldn't be able to
do the same. That very day he hopped
from moleheap to moleheap, turning
over crumbs of soil, hoping to find
a worm. But he wasn't as
lucky as the blackbird.
The mole wasn't likely to
make the same mistake twice.

Another day Cock Robin watched the tits feeding upside down on a half coconut, filled with fat. The agile tits are very expert at this, but robins are not. Cock Robin knew what the tits were feeding on, because he picked up tiny bits of fat that they had dropped to the ground. From time to time during that day he watched the tits feeding, trying to puzzle it out. He knew he couldn't hang upside down like the tits, but he did want some fat, and he spent much of the day watching them and wondering.

By the middle of
the next day he
had solved the
problem, and
the people in the
house watched him
from the kitchen
window. He
hopped along
until he was right
under the coconut,
then he zoomed
up, pecked a
quick mouthful,
and fluttered down
to the ground. He
did this over and
over again until he had eaten all the fat
he wanted. And he did it every day after
that, much to the amusement of the
people at the window.

Cock Robin and the blackbirds trusted
the people in the house, and often
flew to the window ledge for titbits
like mealworms and raisins.

They hopped about there even when the
cat was at the window inside, for they
had learned long ago that he was not
a bird hunter.

One day a grey squirrel leaped on to
the nut dispenser and frightened away
the tits. He clung there for so long,
wrapped round the dispenser, that the
birds became hungry; and hunger made
them bolder. After a while they flew
back to the dispenser and the great tits
perched on him to peck at the peanuts.

While there was room on the dispenser
for one squirrel, there wasn't room
for two. But another squirrel arrived,
and the pair took turn about. While
one clung to the dispenser, with tits
using him as a perch, the other hopped
about below the bird table picking up
anything that was spilled over. A
few days later the owner of the garden
put out whole nuts specially for the
squirrels and the pair soon found them.
When they had eaten all the nuts they
needed for the moment, they stuffed the
others into their mouths and carried
them away to hide them in Squirrel
Wood. Then they were back to their
old tricks, one on the dispenser and
one on the ground below.

Despite the cold weather, most of the birds liked to bathe every day in the bird-bath that had been put out specially for them. All of them drank from it as well. When the water in the bird-bath froze over the owner thawed out the ice with warm water.

When the bath was crowded, each bird was happy to wait its turn, so there was hardly ever any quarrelling. Quite often there would be several birds in the bath at the same time splashing with their wings, while others hopped about nearby shaking the water from their feathers.

With the coming of spring, the birds began to nest. Over in Squirrel Wood the rooks were already busy, and their harsh cawing could be heard all day.

In the garden the blackbirds were the first to nest, and Cock Robin saw the hen carrying beakfuls of dry grass into the big holly tree, while her mate sang from the topmost twig.

The blackbirds were very fond of the big holly tree and there was hardly a year when they didn't nest in it.

Cock Robin was no longer the only robin
in the garden, for earlier in the year
he had allowed a hen to join him.
When she first arrived he puffed out
his red breast at her until he could
be really sure she was a hen.

But this didn't
take him long
and they quickly
settled down
together. Very
soon now they too
would be nesting.

The hen robin built her nest in
the heart of a dense prickly
gooseberry bush. The woodpigeon
laid two white eggs in a flimsy nest of
twigs in a tall hawthorn at the bottom
of the garden. The
starlings, searching
for a nesting place,
examined every hole
in the birch tree
beside the gable of
the house.

All the garden birds were now busy and when Cock Robin's mate was sitting on the eggs, he carried food to her on the nest. The cock woodpigeon flew into the hawthorn every morning to take his turn on the eggs, while the cock blackbird spent most of his time searching for worms in the shrubbery. He was kept busy because his mate now had young.

Like the woodpeckers, blue tits and starlings like to nest in holes in trees. But unlike the woodpeckers, the tits and starlings can't drill out holes for themselves, so they have to find ready-made ones. Both of them wanted one of the holes in the birch tree and there was much angry argument and puffing out of feathers until, in the end, the tits drove the starlings away. The starlings left, not because they were really afraid of the tiny blue tits but because by then they had given up any idea of using that hole anyway.

Cock Robin was alarmed when he saw the
house cat prowling in the garden. The
tits, equally alarmed, scolded him from
a low branch, while the cock blackbird
called *pink pink pink* from
the holly. But the cat
wasn't hunting birds and
soon padded away. In a
few moments the birds had
forgotten him.

A pair of yellowhammers
arrived in the garden and
built their nest among thick
nettles under a gooseberry
bush, not far from the robins.
Every day the cock yellow-
hammer sat on top
of the holly and
sang:
*A-little-bit-
of-bread-and-
no-cheese.*

Cock Robin was just a little bit afraid
the first time he saw the man from the
house digging in the garden near the
nest, where hen robin now had young.
But as the days passed he grew bolder
and bolder, and began to follow the man
about, for he quickly learned that where
the man was digging with his garden fork,
worms were sure to be turned up. Cock
Robin carried the
worms to his mate
on the nest, who
then fed them to
her young.

One day a grey squirrel climbed up to the woodpigeon's nest, hoping to steal her eggs. But the woodpigeon had hatched her eggs and now had two chicks called squeakers. When the squirrel tried to snatch one of them the woodpigeon puffed out her chest and gave him a good cuff in the face with a wing. He then tried to get behind her, but she turned round at the same time and cuffed him with her other wing.

The next time the squirrel came to the garden to look for birds' nests he was chased by the house cat, and Cock Robin, who was sitting on a spade with a beakful of caterpillars, watched the chase.

The cat managed to get his forepaws on the squirrel but couldn't hold him, and he escaped into a tree. The cat climbed after him, but he was no match for a squirrel in the branches and had to give up. On his way back to the house he stopped beside Cock Robin who was on the spade, and looked at him, as though to say: "Well, I didn't do very well that time, did I?"

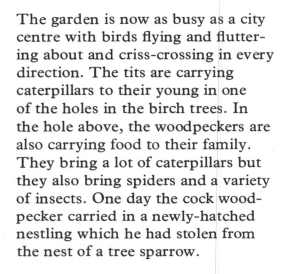

The garden is now as busy as a city
centre with birds flying and fluttering about and criss-crossing in every
direction. The tits are carrying
caterpillars to their young in one
of the holes in the birch trees. In
the hole above, the woodpeckers are
also carrying food to their family.
They bring a lot of caterpillars but
they also bring spiders and a variety
of insects. One day the cock wood-
pecker carried in a newly-hatched
nestling which he had stolen from
the nest of a tree sparrow.

The young robins, now in their first suit of feathers, perch on top of the gooseberry bush waiting to be fed by their parents who bring them earth-worms, caterpillars, insects and spiders. Cock Robin's mate is already busy building a new nest near the old one.

When the owner of the garden was sowing
seeds or transplanting seedlings, Cock
Robin followed him about picking up small
worms and other prey. The man and the
bird had become firm friends and Cock
Robin knew there was always food to be
found easily when he was working in the
garden. Quite often the man had to stop
digging to let Cock Robin pick up a worm
at his feet, and sometimes Cock Robin
would even hop on to his foot.

The yellowhammers were feeding young in their nest among nettles when the hen robin laid the first egg of her second clutch. Her new nest was two feet from the ground in the thick ivy that grew on the garden wall. She laid another three eggs in it then began to sit on them. And there she would sit, day and night, for the next fortnight, leaving Cock Robin to hunt and bring food to her in the nest.

But the birds didn't always succeed in hatching their eggs.

A grey squirrel climbed into an apple tree and robbed the chaffinch's nest, so the bird had to build another nest and lay more eggs.

The blackbird was the next one to be robbed. A magpie stole her second clutch from her new nest in the holly, carrying the eggs away one at a time to eat them. The tits scolded her while hen robin crouched on her nest and escaped the robber's notice. The magpie was nesting in a beech tree in Woodmouse Lane and had young of her own to care for. That is why she stole the eggs of other birds.

Cock Robin had large dark
eyes and could see well at
dusk when the light was
poor. During nesting time he was often
searching for food in the shrubbery
until the owls flew out on their night's
hunting. He was the last bird in the
garden to go to bed and first to start
work in the morning.

A pair of wrens had their nest in the ivy not far from the robins, so they were next door neighbours. The robin and the wren quite often arrived at their nests with food at the same time, so they knew each other well and were very friendly. Now and again Cock Robin would hop on to an ivy leaf above the wren's nest and peep into its small front entrance as if to say hello. Sometimes the wren came to the robin's nest and did the same. The two birds were the best of friends.

The birds knew their own house cat and
were not fooled by a strange one of
the same colour. So when a stray cat
arrived one evening they all joined
to scold him. The stranger was a bird
hunter and killed a young blackbird.

The rat was a much more dangerous enemy
than the cat, especially to birds nesting
on the ground or close to it, and
when a big rat came in from the field
one evening the first thing he did was
to kill a baby robin. The next night
he was back again, prowling in the
garden looking for eggs, or nestlings or
young birds newly fledged. The owner
of the garden saw him and put out a
cage trap to catch him,
but the rat was too
wary to walk into it.

But the house cat had also
seen the rat and knew how
to catch him. Next time
the rat came the cat was
lying in wait.

The cat crouched on the wall and
waited patiently, almost as
though he knew the rat would come
that way. When it did come, the
cat leaped down, and in two bounds
caught it as it tried to escape.

By midsummer the garden was like an aviary, with birds of all ages—adults flying about, or searching for food, and fledglings hunting for themselves or begging from their parents. Cock Robin's chicks were fluttering about and kept him and his mate busy supplying them with food. The chaffinches had their first family out and fully feathered. The blue tits had eight noisy young flying around the birch tree, still begging for food.

A dog weasel came from Wood-mouse Lane and climbed the birch tree to explore the nesting holes. Of course the tits' nesting hole was empty but the woodpeckers still had big nestlings in theirs. When the weasel tried to poke his face into it, the parent woodpeckers flew at him and gave him such a beating with wings and beaks that they knocked him out of the tree.

The fall took the wind
out of the weasel and
ruffled his feelings,
but he wasn't in the
least hurt, and soon he
was padding about the
garden looking for voles
and mice, which were the
prey he liked best and
hunted most. Not long
after that the alert
birds saw him running
back to the lane with
a small rat in his mouth.
Although it was small it
was heavy enough to slow
him down.

On sunny days
peacock and red
admiral and small
tortoiseshell
butterflies fluttered to the
long purple flower spikes of
the buddleias. While the
butterflies sipped nectar,
Cock Robin hunted other
insects among the flower spikes.

Now it was autumn and a flock of
bullfinches arrived in the garden and
gathered in the apple trees. Swallows
from the farm came with their young to
hunt insects and the garden became
busier than ever. When they weren't
hunting, the swallows perched on the
roof of the house or on the telephone
wires. Cock Robin was free again
because his families
had grown up. He
spent most of each
day hunting for
himself and spent less
and less time with
his mate.

Cock Robin hadn't seen much of the hedgehog during most of the summer, but in the autumn it came almost every night, eating everything it could eat because it had to lay on fat for its long winter sleep. One evening it came early and almost took Cock Robin by surprise. He was in the shrubbery turning over leaves with his beak, searching for woodlice, when the hedgehog snatched at him. But he managed to fly up in time, although the hedgehog almost caught him by the tail. If it had caught Cock Robin it would have eaten him.

When the white frosts came once more
Cock Robin flew to the window-sill to
beg for food, and the owner put out
mealworms for him. Soon he was joined
there by the blackbirds who were looking for raisins. The owner put out
raisins for them and the blackbirds
gobbled them quickly.

It was now time for the owner of the
garden to put out food for all the birds
again. On the very first day they learned
that the food was there—peanuts, raisins,
seeds, fat, bread and left-overs from the
kitchen. Once more all roads led to the
bird table, which became the busiest place
in the neighbourhood. But Cock Robin and
the blackbirds still flew to the window-
sill for their mealworms and raisins, and
gave great pleasure to all the people in
the house. They were the only birds who
came there. Not even the bold starlings
would face the cat at the window.

Birds don't usually sing in winter, but
each morning and evening Cock Robin
perched near the kitchen window to sing
a sweet, talkative little song, which
the people in the house began to think
he was singing only for them.

ISBN 0 00 123287 8
Text copyright © 1978 David Stephen
Illustrations copyright © 1978 Marjorie Blamey
Printed and made in Great Britain